LARGE PRINT

Crosswords

Over 100 puzzles

AURA

This edition published in 2012
by Baker & Taylor (UK) Limited,
Bicester, Oxfordshire

Copyright © 2012 Arcturus Publishing Limited
26/27 Bickels Yard, 151–153 Bermondsey Street
London SE1 3HA

Puzzles copyright © 2012 Puzzle Press Ltd

ISBN: 978-1-84858-463-1
AD002215EN

Printed in Indonesia